SUNSET
IN SEPTEMBER

FROSTED LEAVES

PEACE ROSE

SNAKE'S
LILY

£2.20

Judy

FOR GIRLS

Printed and Published in Great Britain by D. C. THOMSON & CO., LTD.,
185 Fleet Street, London, EC4A 2HS. © D. C. THOMSON & CO., LTD., 1984.
1SBN 0-85116-300-9

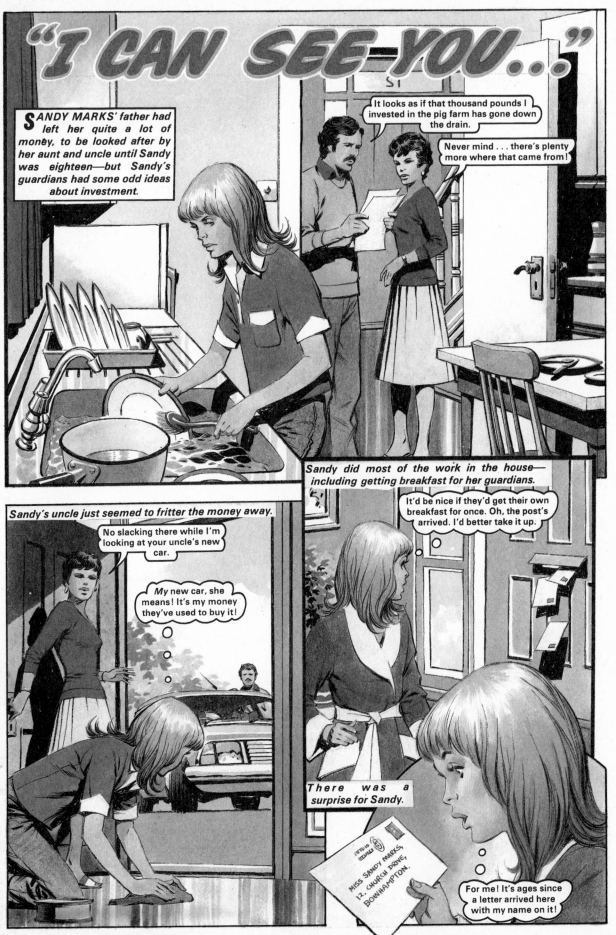

"I CAN SEE-YOU..."

SANDY MARKS' father had left her quite a lot of money, to be looked after by her aunt and uncle until Sandy was eighteen—but Sandy's guardians had some odd ideas about investment.

It looks as if that thousand pounds I invested in the pig farm has gone down the drain.

Never mind . . . there's plenty more where that came from!

Sandy did most of the work in the house—including getting breakfast for her guardians.

It'd be nice if they'd get their own breakfast for once. Oh, the post's arrived. I'd better take it up.

Sandy's uncle just seemed to fritter the money away.

No slacking there while I'm looking at your uncle's new car.

My new car, she means! It's my money they've used to buy it!

There was a surprise for Sandy.

MISS SANDY MARKS, 12. CHURCH DRIVE, BONHAMPTON.

For me! It's ages since a letter arrived here with my name on it!

5

6

7

8

9

.John starts to carve a puppet's head.

BEHIND THE SCENES AT THE LITTLE ANGEL MARIONETTE THEATRE.

Opened in 1961 by John Wright, the Little Angel is one of the very few permanent puppet theatres in Britain. John is shown here with his wife, Lyndie.

Here are some scenes from today's performance of " THE LITTLE MERMAID ", adapted from the Hans Andersen story.

If you have the opportunity, the Little Angel is well worth a visit, with regular performances throughout the year. The address is:- 14 DAGMAR PASSAGE, CROSS STREET, ISLINGTON, LONDON, N1 2DN—or telephone 01-226 1787.

The Little Mermaid has fallen in love with the handsome Prince, whose life she has saved. She makes a bargain with the Sea Witch, who will turn her into a human in exchange for her voice.

The cast , ready to go on stage.

But the King wishes the Prince to marry the beautiful Princess Jasmine.

The Prince falls in love with Princess Jasmine, while the heartbroken Little Mermaid looks on.

10

ON STRINGS

The Giant— a character in the play " The Nine Pointed Crown ".

Repairing a string puppet is a skilled task.

Operators at work during a performance.

These evil-looking creatures are the Sea Witch's attendants.

High view of the last act, in which the Little Mermaid sacrifices her own life for the Prince's happiness.

The Little Mermaid as a human. She cannot speak, and, should the Prince abandon her, she will become no more than a wisp of foam in the sea.

The show is over, and, after his moment of glory, the King goes back into his dust bag until the next performance.

11

LESLEY ARNOT, a talented young dancer, was about to audition for a part in a new musical show.

CASTING TO-DAY

Rosita

At last, it was Lesley's turn—

There's plenty of competition, but I'm going to audition for the lead just the same. Even if I don't get that, I might still be in the chorus.

She's good. Lacks polish—but there's plenty of talent. Even looks the part.

Later, Lesley couldn't believe her luck.

Congratulations, Miss Arnot. You've got the leading part. It'll be hard work, but we believe you'll be a success.

Wow!

Later—

The musical was based on the true story of Rosita, a young Spanish dancer, a hard ruthless girl, who, after becoming rich and famous, died a tragic death.

The story is certainly dramatic. The girl obviously had a strong personality to have become such a powerful figure.

This is one of the dresses Rosita wore during her dancing career. There are a few more here which we can use for the first night gala performance until copies are made.

12

ROSITA
CASTING

During a dress rehearsal, Lesley wore one of Rosita's costumes.

How beautiful this dress makes me look. After I've appeared in this musical *I* shall be famous and rich!

My partner nearly dropped me twice and he's been out of step once already!

I won't dance another step with him! And as for the pianist—I want him replaced!

Lesley flounced off stage.

What's got into her? She used to be such a nice girl!

13

The GUARDIANS

SIGRID JOHANSSON had arranged to spend some of her holidays with her grandmother in a remote Swedish village, but already she was beginning to regret it.

What a dump! It looks as if everyone and everything's fast asleep! I wish I'd stayed in Stockholm!

Sigrid's grandmother made her welcome.

Sigrid! It's so nice of you to come and stay with me for a little while. I hope you won't be bored.

Of course not, Grandma. I'll help you round the house.

Next evening—

Don't pour hot water down the drain!

Whyever not, Grandma?

It's not wise to disturb the Vaeltar.

The old dear must be going potty!

Next morning, Sigrid was in for another surprise.

What's the matter, Grandma? Have you spilled something?

The Vaeltar were here last night. They probably wondered who you were. The floor must be clean for them.

Puzzled, Sigrid went downstairs.

I don't know what Grandma means, but somehow I don't like it! Oh, here's a letter for her.

It's such a nuisance! From my lawyer in Umaa. I shall have to go there, I'm afraid. Telephone for a taxi, would you please, dear?

Soon—

I shan't be back until tomorrow morning, Sigrid. Will you be all right?

Don't worry about me— I'll be fine.

17

Later— Nothing but rubbish on television—hello, there's somebody at the door.

Sorry to bother you, but we're camping nearby. Could we have some water?

Yes, of course. Come in.

But, once inside— Hey! What d'you think you're doing?

Keep quiet, unless you want to get hurt!

That afternoon was sheer torture for Sigrid.

These old codgers always have money stashed away somewhere!

You're not going anywhere! We know the old lady won't be back until tomorrow! Get us some food ready!

The old girl must have some cash somewhere—and we'll find it!

Night fell at last.

Nothing! She must have hidden it too well!

I wonder if the girl knows where it is!

Sigrid ran upstairs and locked herself in her room.

We don't have to worry about her escaping any more, Soren!

Right, Erik—we might as well spend the night here. The beds will be softer than the forest.

Sigrid lay awake, unable to sleep, then, in the small hours of the morning—

What's that? I hear voices!

Sigrid's blood froze as the noises grew louder.

Hey! What the—?

Finally, Sigrid slept, until—

Are you all right, Sigrid? I just got back and I found the front door wide open.

Oh, Grandma! I'm so glad you're back!

They've got me! They're all over the—

What's going on in there? It sounds as if there's an army of them!

Downstairs, another shock awaited Sigrid.

Two intruders ransacked the house— but it's all been mended and tidied, apart from those odd little footprints!

The Vaeltar got rid of them for us, Sigrid.

The old legends tell us that the Vaeltar are house-spirits the size of small children. They live in the drains, under the floors, and behind the panelling, and they protect the home from evil.

Just then, the telephone rang. It was the police.

Tell Mrs Johansson we've just arrested two hikers who tried to rob her last night. They're gibbering about being attacked by a gang of dwarves.

Now then, Sigrid, they like the house to be clean. Come along.

Yes, Grandmother.

Sometimes it's not a good thing to make fun of old legends—especially when they leave footprints!

THE END

19

TRACE OFF IF YOU DON'T WANT TO CUT YOUR " JUDY " BOOK.

20

Little Awful Annie

You saw that the bag was empty, Aunt Agnes. Now what's inside?

Eek! It's a great big spider!

LITTLE Annie Wharton had high hopes of becoming a comedy magician, and, at every opportunity, she insisted on "entertaining" her relatives.

You can help with my next trick, Uncle George. Don't I have an electrifying handshake?

Aaaah! It's an electric-shock machine!

I think it's time we went home, George.

You're surely not leaving? The show isn't over yet!

Oh, yes, it is!

Next day, Annie was in the town.

Nobody appreciates my act! Hello! What's this? A talent show? With that TV comedian? This could be my big chance!

TALENT CONTEST PRESENTED BY BERNIE HAMILTON

That should be a good show. Bernie Hamilton's daughter's appearing in it, as well.

Adela's the same age as me. I've seen her on TV. Wouldn't it be great if I won the contest? I'll put my name down.

But someone else was interested in the Hamiltons.

That comic's worth a fortune. If we kidnap his daughter, we can make a packet.

Kidnapping's a serious crime!

We won't kidnap her really. We'll just take her to a snack bar for an hour then collect the money. I've seen it on a film. It's easy.

On the night of the talent contest—

My agent and a top manager will be in the audience tonight, Adela. They've come to see you.

An agent and a manager? This really is going to be my big chance!

Annie persuaded Adela to assist—

Hey presto! Now you know how Nelson feels on top of his column, Adela!

Get this bird off me!

Adela's father stepped in to stop the act.

I'll have to put a stop to this!

Well, thank you Annie Wharton, and now—

Just one moment! Observe that this box is completely empty, ladies and gentlemen.

If you'll just hold that, Mr Hamilton. I tap the box and utter the magic word . . . shazzam!

I don't think . . .

We ran out of pigeons, so I bought some eggs.

Annie went out for a breath of air after her act, and—

Er—hello. Are you Adela Hamilton?

STAGE DOOR

These must be the two showbiz men.

Oh, you've come to talk business, have you? I'll be right with you.

And unless you pay five thousand pounds, you'll never see your daughter again, Mr Hamilton!

You haven't been kidnapped, have you, Adela?

No, Dad—at least not the last time I looked!

The kidnappers took Annie to a nearby café.

Have another! These sweets are a hot favourite with me!

Graaagh! My mouth!

I'll go and make a 'phone call!

That's her third hamburger! She's costing us a fortune!

Not only that, she's the wrong girl! We'll have to find out her 'phone number and ring her real parents!

My 'phone number? Oh, you want it for the contract? Could I have another cola, please?

Er . . . yes, yes, of course.

But, of course, Annie's parents were at the theatre. Only her elder brother was at home.

If you want to see her again, it'll cost you five hundred pounds.

Another of Annie's stupid practical jokes!

Forget it, chum! You can keep her!

That's one of my best tricks! It brings the house down!

Look, how about fifty pounds? A fiver, then? Just to cover the petrol and hamburgers?

Come on, we're getting out of here!

Not before time! I knew this wouldn't work!

Well, what d'you say? Did you like the act? Do I get the contract?

Er . . . excuse us . . .

Important appointment . . .

Huh! What's got into them?

But, someone was looking for Annie.

Hey, where have you been? They're presenting the prizes. You came fourth.

Only fourth?

STAGE DOOR

Moments later—

There wasn't going to be a fourth prize, but we've decided that Annie Wharton deserves a special award!

I knew it! I've made a hit!

A pair of opera glasses, Annie. See if you can see your parents in the audience.

Thanks!

I bet they'll be proud of me now!

I can't see a thing!

Perhaps they need adjusting Here, let me . . .

Annie Wharton, ladies and gentlemen—a great little joker!

I suppose he thinks that's funny!

THE END

Boomtime For BRITISH BANGERS!

The good old-fashioned banger is still one of Britain's favourite foods. There's nothing quite like a plateful of bangers and mash.

However, there are many ways to eat sizzling sausages. Here are three recipes for delicious sausage savoury dips that will make any party or barbecue go with a bang!

Recipes by kind permission of The Meat Promotion Executive.

Grill or fry your sausages and then try one of the following dips.

MUSTARD SAUCE

36 g. butter
25 g. flour
375 ml. (¾ pt.) milk
Salt and pepper
1 level teaspoon dry mustard
1 tablespoon wine vinegar
1 level teaspoon caster sugar

Melt the butter gently, then, off the heat, stir in the flour. Carefully blend in the milk, and, stirring all the time, bring to the boil. Allow to boil for 2-3 minutes.

Blend the mustard with the vinegar until smooth and add to the sauce. Season to taste, and add the caster sugar.

BARBECUE SAUCE

1 teaspoon chilli powder
1 teaspoon celery salt
2 tablespoons soft brown sugar
2 tablespoons wine vinegar
2 tablespoons Worcestershire sauce
3 tablespoons tomato ketchup
125 ml. beef stock
Tabasco to taste
Salt and freshly-ground black pepper

Combine all the ingredients in a bowl.

PROVENCAL SAUCE

1 medium-sized onion, finely chopped
2 tablespoons cooking oil
200 g. can tomatoes
1 tablespoon tomato puree
½ teaspoon dried basil
1 clove garlic, crushed
Pinch caster sugar
Salt and pepper

Fry onion gently in oil for 5 minutes. Add tomatoes, puree, basil and garlic, and season to taste with sugar, salt and pepper. Simmer for 5 minutes.

Always ask an adult before using the cooker.

Speaking with Tongues

FAY GARFIELD wasn't dim—she just found it hard to concentrate on her schoolwork. It all seemed so dull. Her teachers, however, didn't understand Fay's feelings!

Fay, this school report is even worse than the last one!

I'm sorry, Dad. I do try—but it all seems so boring!

Boring or not, if you don't pay a bit more attention to your work, you'll regret it when you leave school!

I'll try harder, Mum, I promise. 'Bye!

A few days later, at breakfast—

We've won first prize in a competition—a holiday abroad for two!

That's great! Er—only for two?

I think we can just afford to pay the extra, and take you along—if you deserve it!

If I deserve it?

Exams start next week, don't they? If you can improve on last term, you can come along!

For days, Fay buried herself in her books.

It's late, Fay! Time you were in bed!

I shan't be sorry to pack in this history study!

All right, Mum. Good night.

Next day, Fay spotted an article in a magazine.

It says here that you can learn while you're asleep! It's got to be easier than all this swotting!

So, the night before the history exam—

I'll record all this stuff on a cassette.

The signing of the Magna Carta marked a turning-point in English civil law, in that the king's powers were . . .

And—

I've set it to switch off later, while I'm asleep. If this works, I'll soon be top of the class!

25

Cora Cupid

CORA CARTER, of Palewell Comprehensive, fancied herself a born matchmaker, often with dire results. Most people tried to escape her attentions, but Gary Evans actually asked her for help.

The fact is, Cora, I can get dates all right, but no girl ever goes out with me more than once.

Hmmm! Must be something you're doing wrong without realising it. This means a personal, on-the-spot investigation. Now, this is what we're going to do . . .

Later—

Cora, I appreciate that you want to help Gary, but I can't see why you actually have to *date* him.

It's very simple, Phil. He's going to behave with me the same way he behaves with every other girl he's ever dated. That way, I'll be able to find out what's wrong.

That Saturday afternoon—

Right, Gary, so what's it to be? There's the disco, the pictures, or we could have some hamburgers at Maxie's.

What about a nice walk down to the town square?

Walk?

Nothing like a stroll on a brisk afternoon to blow the cobwebs away.

Oh, let's just sit here in the fresh air and watch the world go by. There's nothing I like better than that.

But it's freezing!

At that moment—

Oh, look, Gary . . . hot chestnuts! Could we have some to warm us up?

Er—we'll have one bag between us. No sense in stuffing ourselves. Or, wait a minute—what about those burnt ones you've put aside? How much are they?

10 PENCE A BAG

Great! I got them for five pence!

Er . . . Gary . . . how about getting some cola to go with these? One bottle between us, of course!

Thirsty, are you? Lucky we're right near the drinking fountain. There's nothing like a drink of cool, clear water.

Gary, the experiment is over! I know now why you never got a second date with a girl!

You're a *miser*, that's why! *Stingy,* in other words. S . . . T . . . I . . . N . . . GEE! And if you think I'm going to condemn some poor, innocent girl to go through what I've been through today, you can forget it!

Later, talking it over with her boyfriend, Phil, Cora had an attack of conscience.

I shouldn't have said what I did. After all, he came to me looking for help—and it's not his fault he's mean. It's just his character.

Well, the only thing you can do is find him a girlfriend as stingy as he is.

So Cora asked around among the girls she knew.

There's no-one like that at Palewell—but over at St Cyprian's there's a girl called Tillie Davis, and she's known as Tightwad Tillie.

With a nickname like that, she's bound to be as mean as Gary, if not more!

As it happened, the Palewell Netball Team were playing home to St Cyprian's the following Saturday.

How did you get Gary to come?

Easy. I reminded him it was a cheap day out.

Look, that's Tilly Davis over there. All alone, too.

Cora moved smoothly into action.

Hello! Welcome to Palewell. On your own, I see. Why not join us?

Let me introduce you . . . this is Gary Evans.

Well, er . . .

Gary, this is Tight . . . I mean, Tilly Davis, of St Cyprian's. I'm sure she'd like to be shown over our sports grounds.

Sure! Come on, then, Tillie.

But . . . but . . .

Went like a dream! It gives such a sense of satisfaction to bring two people together who have everything in common.

Hi! Have any of you seen a girl who was sitting here a few minutes ago?

It's a friend of ours—Tillie Davis. She's treated us all to these drinks and doughnuts, but now she seems to have vanished.

You . . . you say Tillie Davis, of St Cyprian's, paid for this lot? But . . . but isn't she the one who's known as Tightwad Tillie?

That's just a St Cyprian's in-joke. Like the way they call very short people Lofty.

Or fat people Slim. You see, Tillie Davis is the biggest spendthrift that ever lived.

Dead generous . . . well, you can see. Gets through her week's pocket-money in the first two days.

Then gets through everyone else's—especially her boyfriends'. That's why she can't *keep* a boyfriend these days.

Oh, no!

As a matter of fact, we hear there's a girl at Palewell who's a whizz at playing Cupid, and we were wondering if perhaps she could find Tillie a Palewell boy who was as much of a spender as she was.

Where are you going, Cora?

Just going to attend to a little matter!

Poor Gary! I've got to rescue him—I've got to!

Gary!

Hello, Cora! Sit down and help yourself to some refreshments. Make it fast, though, because afterwards Tillie and I are off to see the film at the Palace.

Gary! You . . . you have to pay to get into the Palace, remember?

Oh, well, we only live once. When pocket-money's gone, it's gone. Might as well enjoy it while you've got it.

I heard all that, Cora—and I don't mind telling you, I just don't understand it!

I'm only just beginning to understand it myself—and I'm supposed to be the expert!

It's quite simple, Phil, as you'd know if you studied these things.

And, naturally, I knew what I was doing from the very beginning.

The End

A Link with the Past

ANNE DRUMMOND had never known her Victorian parents, and had been brought up by the housekeeper, whom she called Nanny, in the remote manor house in the highlands of Scotland. They also had a cook and gardener, and Anne wanted for nothing. But, about one thing, Nanny had always been firm....

Anne, you must promise me that you will never, ever go out of the grounds.

All right, Nanny, I won't, if you don't want me to.

But, as Anne grew up, she became curious.

This is a picture of Queen Victoria, Anne.

But it's only a drawing. I wonder what she looks like in real life.

Why can't I visit these places? I'd love to go to Edinburgh—or even London. Perhaps I'd really see Queen Victoria then.

After her lessons, Anne went for a walk in the grounds.

George, do you know why I'm not allowed to leave the grounds?

Now then, Miss Anne, you know Nanny's got your best interests at heart.

Then, one day when Anne was by the old, rusting gates of the estate—

Good day, mistress. Could you direct me to Glendoury Farm, please?

I'm afraid I've never heard of it, sir.

The first person I've ever seen from outside! Now's my chance!

You see, I'm not allowed out.

Not allowed? What d'you mean? Are you a prisoner?

I suppose I am, in a way. Oh, if only I could get to town I might find out who my real family are.

The doctor, a stranger to the area, was troubled by Anne's story.

All I want is to be able to talk to someone in the village.

Well, I don't know many people yet, but my partner, Doctor MacDonald, knows everyone. Perhaps he could help you.

There—the gate chain was nearly rusted through. I'll take you to Doctor MacDonald. He'll be able to help you, I'm sure.

Oh, thank you!

The young doctor took Anne to the village.

So this is what the village looks like!

Doctor MacDonald—here's a girl needs your help to find out about her family . . . Anne Drummond.

34

Anne Drummond? Good grief, man, d'you not know about that family? Listen . . .

All these houses . . . and shops . . . and people walking about! I could spend a week here!

But Anne didn't get the chance.

Where are we going? What did Doctor MacDonald say?

He said I must take you straight back home!

When they reached the house, the doctor was still intrigued.

You say you live with your nanny, the cook and the gardener? No relatives at all?

None. Why don't you come and meet them? It's the least you could do!

The doctor agreed, and they went up to the house.

Nanny! Nanny! Where are you? We've got a visitor! Let's see if she's in her room, Doctor.

Anne had always been forbidden to enter Nanny's room, but she did so now.

She's not here! It looks as if no-one's been here in years! And it's so cold!

World Of Wildfowl

ONE hundred and forty thousand visitors in one year; that's the number of people who visit the Wildfowl Trust Sanctuary in Arundel, in Sussex. The bird family there is a large one—over a thousand residents, with lots of visiting birds, too—and many of them are rare or foreign species. However, common ducks, geese and swans are also kept on the fifty-acre site, to attract rare or migrating birds and to give people a chance to watch them closely. If you like watching the antics of ducks and geese, you'll really enjoy a visit to Arundel, or one of the other Wildfowl Centres. Here we show you some of the most attractive birds at the Arundel Centre . . .

This is a Hawaiian Goose, sometimes called a Ne-Ne—for that's how it sounds. In 1952, there were only 42 of these geese left alive in the world, so the Sanctuary is helping to rescue them from becoming extinct.

Moorhens certainly aren't an endangered species, but most people stop to watch their antics. You may find some on your local pond.

A swan has a longer neck than a goose, but swans and geese belong to the same species. This is the aptly-named Black-Necked Swan.

This fellow attracts by his beauty. He's a Mandarin Duck, and as exotic looking as his name would lead you to expect.

Ducks are generally small birds with short necks. This picture shows Barrow's Goldeneye, which comes from Iceland.

These Black Swans are from Australia. The young ones are about ten weeks old.

Another duck, a South American Chiloe Wigean . . .

. . . and a Pochard. Unlike geese, most ducks walk clumsily on land. Ducks have shield-shaped scales on their legs. The scales on the legs of swans and geese are like a net.

This North American Swan had a noisy greeting for one of the sanctuary staff—someone he obviously regarded as a friend.

This duck, with his lovely blue beak, is a North American Ruddy.

Part of the Sanctuary is wild and no-one is allowed to enter. Visitors look out from a hut that has a narrow opening along one side. That way, they can watch birds that would take flight at the slightest disturbance.

This is another goose, with a name that reflects his looks—he's a Bar- Headed Goose.

An obviously happy group of Orinoco Geese. These were the first Orinoco Geese to be bred in captivity for fifteen years, so, naturally, the staff at the Arundel Sanctuary were very proud of them.

**If you happen to be in Sussex and would like to visit the Sanctuary, the address is:—
Mill Road, Arundel, Sussex.**

WEEDY WENDY

WENDY HARGREAVES was a laughing stock at St Margaret's School. She was small and slight, and a dismal failure at all sports.

Look at Weedy Wendy —last, as usual!

I don't know why she bothers! Latin's more in her line!

Then, one day, an ex-pupil of St Margaret's died, and—

Dame Elizabeth Mountford has left her great manor house to the school. So, from next term, we shall be leaving these old buildings and moving there.

An army of tradesmen went to work on the rooms of the old manor house . . . well, most of them.

We've tried, but we can't open the door to this room, Dr Miles. We don't want to damage it, of course.

Yes, I know. The door is mentioned in Dame Elizabeth's will.

In order for the school to inherit the entire building, one of our pupils must open the door and take whatever is inside.

CUM CONVEN
ARGENTUM ET
CUM STABIT LEAEN:
EMOLUE ROSA DONATA

One of your girls? My strongest man couldn't budge it!

In school, there were countless rumours about what was in the sealed room.

The old girl was really rich. I bet it's a casket of diamonds or something!

It's an odd kind of test, opening a locked door.

You won't get a crack at opening it, Wendy! You couldn't open a paper bag!

However, some of us are strong in body, Dr Miles. Some—like Dame Elizabeth—are strong in mind.

Yes—and she became a minister in the government! Nobody laughed at her, once she left school!

At the start of the following term, Wendy overheard a conversation between the Head and a visitor.

Kind of you to perform our opening ceremony for the new building, Miss Graham.

My pleasure, Dr Miles. I taught Dame Elizabeth, you know. She was a small girl, not strong at all. The other pupils laughed at her because she was no good at sports.

The following day, the opening ceremony took place.

Now, Mrs Graham, who taught at St Margaret's sixty years ago, will perform the opening ceremony.

Thank you, Dr Miles. Now, someone must open the sealed door. First, Carol Johnson, head of school.

It's no good! It won't move!

CUM CONVENIENT
ARGENTUM EF
CUM STABIT ELS
EL QUE ROSA DON
TUM PORTA AR
OMNIUM IN LUCA

Carol's the sports captain. If she can't open it, no-one can!

Several of the senior girls tried the door, but none could open it.

Wendy had been studying the inscription on the door, and—

May I try, Dr Miles?

You, Wendy?

Let her.

41

Wendy went to the door.

The door can't be opened by strength alone, so it must require something else. Look at the Latin motto under the shield.

"When Gold and Silver come together, when the lioness stands and is given the rose, then let the door open and what is inside is yours." That's how it translates.

CUM CONVENIENT
ARGENTUM ET AURUM
CUM STABIT LEAENA
ETQUE ROSA DONATA
TUM PORTA APERIETUR
OMNIA INCLUSA ERUNT TUA

The lion is gold, so it ought to slide towards the silver. Yes, it moves!

CUM CONVENIEN
ARGENTUM ET AURUM

If I twist the lioness upright and "give" it the rose, by sliding it towards it, like this . . . yes, it's moving!

CUM CONVEN
ARGENTUM

The door swung noiselessly open, to reveal—

The School Enterprise Cup! It's been lost for thirty years! It was presented by Dame Elizabeth's father.

And Dame Elizabeth was the last winner. Remember what I said about being strong in mind, Dr Miles?

The cup was awarded for the most intelligent appraisal of difficult circumstances. We'll have your name engraved on it, Wendy!

A worthy winner if ever there was one!

One thing's for sure—nobody at this school will ever laugh at "Weedy Wendy" again!

THE END

42

What a beautiful old sign. This must have been an inn.

Hello, young lady. Found the old inn sign, have you?

In the old days there was a big harbour at Morefleet, with ships docking from all over the world. The crews used to stay at the "Traveller's Rest".

It's a super old sign. Could I buy it?

You can have it, if you want it. It didn't bring the last owners much luck!

Once back at home, Jeannie's father cleaned up the sign.

Jeannie's right—it's a much better sign than "The Dead End".

Doesn't it look great? That'll bring the customers in!

Ye Traveller's Rest

The week before the grand opening, it was Jeannie's parents' wedding anniversary.

Sure you'll be all right, Jeannie?

Of course! Have a good time. I'm going to have an early night, anyway.

What a beautiful night. And the sign looks super in the moonlight. I just know that we're going to have good luck here!

But Jeannie had hardly dropped off to sleep, when—

Hello! Anybody there? Got a bed for a weary traveller?

Oh! Somebody at the door!

Sorry, we're not—

But why not? Everything's ready, and we open next week anyway. And what a pleasant surprise for Mum and Dad!

Jeannie dressed quickly and let the stranger in.

Would you like to sign the register?

Sign, girlie? Jack Kelham don't sign anything!

I'll be wanting a meal, and a pot of good ale. Can ye manage that?

Oh, he can't read or write!

Yes . . . yes, of course. Go into the bar.

Jeannie quickly rustled up a meal.

Have you come far?

Aye, lass, just off the "Karelia" out of Newfoundland, and spent hundreds of miles dreaming o' clapping eyes on the welcome sign of the "Traveller's Rest"!

What's a seaman doing here eighty miles from the sea? And how can he have been here before? Oh! There's someone else at the door! I hope it's Dad!

45

But it wasn't.

I-I'm sorry, but—

Ahab! Giorgio! Thought ye'd never get here! More food, more ale, lass!

Jeannie did as she was bid.

Oh, Mum and Dad—come home soon!

As Jeannie returned with the food—

Did ye learn to reef a topsail this voyage, Giorgio, eh?

Topsail? That's a hundred years ago and more! Oh, no! Another knock on the door!

When Jeannie opened the door—

Is Ahab Crane here, girl?

If ye believe in God, Ahab Crane, make peace with him now!

Aaaaah!

I must get help!

Jeannie rushed upstairs to the phone, but, just then—

Mum and Dad! I must stop them coming in! I daren't shout!

Jeannie leapt for the swinging sign.

Oh, no! It's coming away from the wall!

Ye Traveller's Rest

Fortunately, it was only a short drop to the ground, but the sign was completely smashed.

The noise . . . the fighting! They stopped just as the inn-sign smashed!

Jeannie hurriedly told her story, but, when they went inside—

There's nobody here, Jeannie— except you! Are you sure you're feeling all right?

But they were here! That's why I cooked the food!

Well, somebody was here!

Ye Traveller's

They left this to pay for the food! A gold dubloon!

It was the sign—the old sign from the seafarers' inn, that brought them here! When it smashed, they must have gone back . . . back to where they came from!

The Inn is called Greensleeves now, and it does very well—but it doesn't entertain many seamen these days.

GREENSLEEVES

THE END

THE PAPER RAILWAY

The Sittingbourne and Kemsley Light Railway, in Kent, was formerly used to carry wood pulp to the local paper mill. It has a charm of its own, as Clare discovered when she spent the day there.

"Changing the points."

"All aboard!"

"And off we go!"

"Just time for a few souvenirs."

ST. OLAFS

We'll be finished soon. The bus is always empty for the last few stops.

SALLY BAIRD'S father ran a country bus service in the wilds of Norfolk, and, during her school holidays, she decided to earn some pocket-money as his conductress.

But, this particular Monday night—

That's odd! I didn't see that passenger get on! And it's not raining outside—yet she's dripping wet!

"TO THE STATION!"

Sally went forward to collect the mysterious passenger's fare.

Wenbury station, please.

That station was closed down years ago! And that's an old penny she's offering!

Sally told her father, who stopped the bus, and—

What girl, Sally? There's no-one there. Are you sure you didn't drop off to sleep and dream it?

She was there! She gave me this old penny!

That's a ten pence piece!

Oh! But it was—I suppose I must have been dreaming!

The following night, at the same point in the route—

It's the same girl! Yet I'd swear we never picked her up!

I'm sorry, but Wenbury station was closed down years ago—and those old pennies aren't legal tender any more, I'm afraid.

To the station! Please! The station!

Dad! It's that girl I saw last night! She's still asking for the station—please come and explain to her!

But I tell you, I haven't picked anyone up!

See? No-one's there.

But look at the puddle of rain-water under the seat—although it's dry tonight! And this *is* an old penny! The date is 1917!

The following night, Sally saw the girl again.

I don't know who you are, but can you tell me what's the matter? Why are you crying?

The station! I must go to the station! Tonight is the last train!

Then—

The station! This is my stop!

She's right—we've stopped! And that really is the old ruined station out there!

Wait! I'm coming with you!

Where's Dad got to? And it's raining cats and dogs out there! A few moments ago it was a beautiful night!

When Sally followed the mystery girl into the station—

But—but this isn't possible! The station's a ruin! And, anyway, the railways don't use steam engines any more!

Rooted to the spot, Sally watched the girl as the train stopped.

Is James Machin on this train? Do any of you know James Machin?

James? Aye, I know him—or at least, I did know him.

The soldier said something to the girl that Sally couldn't hear, then—

No! No! No!

Stop! The train's moving!

Aaaaaaah!

Careful, miss! Look where you—Oh, no!

She seemed to be so upset that she didn't know where she was going. But why?

Just then, Sally heard a familiar voice.

Sally! What are you doing there? Come on, I've mended the fuel line. All aboard.

Dad? But I . . . what's happened here? Can I have imagined it all?

Fancy the old bus breaking down at this time of night. Where have you been? You're soaked!

I-I don't know, Dad! I really don't know!

Back home, Sally asked her grandmother if she had ever heard of James Machin.

James Machin? Now that's a name I haven't heard in over fifty years! James was a farmer's son and he was engaged to Maud Colbeck, the daughter of the vicar at Fenwick. But before they could marry, he had to go and fight in France, in the Great War . . .

"When the war was over, he wrote to Maud saying that he would be coming back from France and she was to meet him at Wenbury station. There were three troop-trains to Wenbury, on Monday, Tuesday, and Wednesday of a week that was the wettest in living memory. Each night Maud took a penny bus-ride to the station, only to find on the last night that James, having survived so much, had drowned on the way back from France. Overcome with grief, she stumbled off the platform in the path of the train."

She was buried in the little churchyard between Fenwick and Wenbury.

Next day, Sally and her grandmother went to Maud's grave.

Look, Granny—the war had been over for months when James Machin died! And the 13th July! That was yesterday!

MAUD COLBECK
3rd APR. 1897
13th JULY 1919

They cleared the weeds from the gravestone, and—

There you are, Maud. I hope you found your James, at last!

THE END

PINS 'N' THINGS

If you're like most girls, you probably never have enough money to buy those little presents that you want to give throughout the year. However, for only a few pence, you can make this lovely PINS 'N' THINGS holder—an ideal gift for Mum, Gran or any of your friends. If you don't want to use our designs, then you can draw your own. After you've made one, you'll realise how simple the job is.

1. Trace off either of the designs onto stiff white card. Cut along the solid lines and fold along the dotted ones.

2. Make three cuts, each 2 mm. long, in either side of the card, where shown. Wind three different coloured threads between the cuts. Place needles and safety pins on card where shown.

3. Colour in both parts of the drawing, fold at the dotted lines and your PINS 'N' THINGS is ready to use.

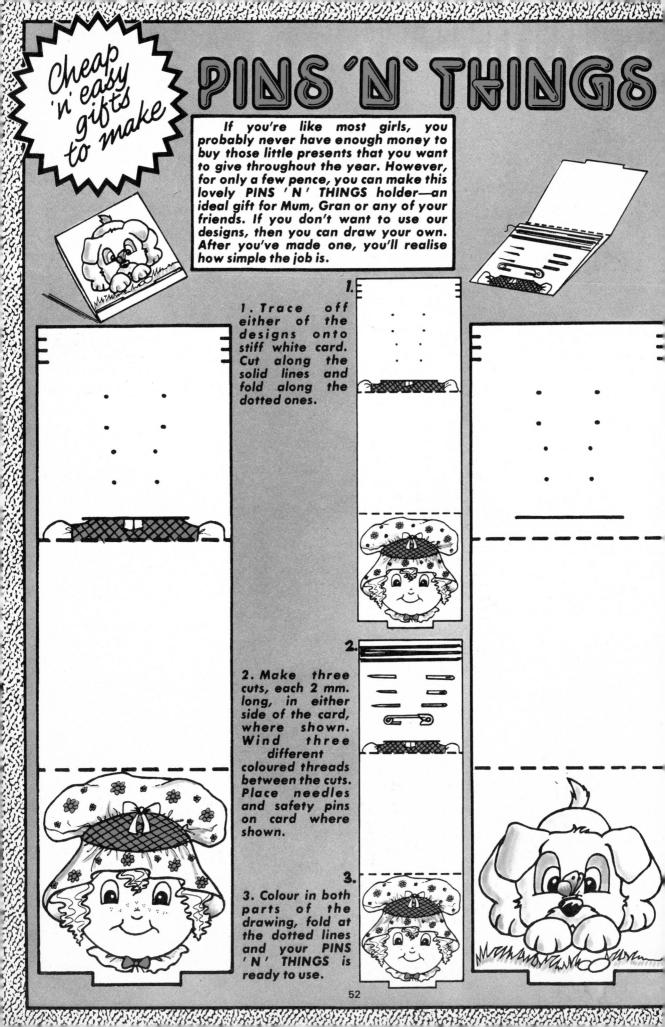

THE STEEL TREE

What do you think of this, Mother Goose?

MOTHER GOOSE kept a small shop specialising in items from the world of fairy tales and nursery rhymes. One day she was visited by Pat Black, a young art student, carrying a small tree modelled in metal.

A little nut tree, with a silver nutmeg and a golden pear! It's beautiful! Did you make it?

Yes—more's the pity! I'm in my final year at the college, studying fine metalwork, but I can't sell my work. The craft shops tell me it's jewellery, and the jewellers tell me it's craft! I wondered if you'd try to sell it for me.

I'll try—although it's a bit more expensive than my usual things.

Thanks!

The following day—

May I have a look in that shop, Papa?

Of course, Maria. Perhaps there we shall find you a gift to take back to Mama in Madrid.

The man, a Spanish diplomat, was captivated by the little nut tree.

A beautiful piece of work, señora. My wife will be delighted. I have been here on a trade delegation from the Spanish Embassy.

There you are. Have you enjoyed being in Britain?

Oh, yes, thank you. Papa brought me along as a special treat. We are going home tonight.

The following morning, Pat Booth was cycling through the outskirts of town, when—

My little nut tree! Mother Goose has sold it already!

55

JUNIOR NANNY

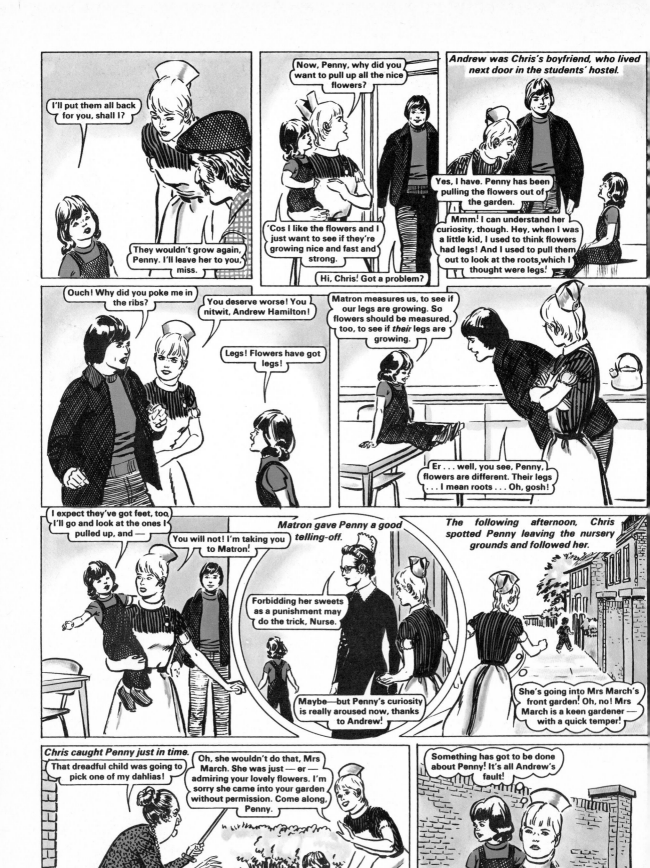

58

Later, when Andrew came to visit Chris, she was still angry.

I'm sorry about my thoughtless remarks to Penny, Chris. Look, how about letting her have a garden of her own? Maybe she'd take a pride in it, in her flowers, and —

Flowers? They wouldn't stand a chance! She's hooked on pulling flowers up, to see their legs grow!

If that's the best you can come up with, then you'd better shut up!

All right. Here — I bought these for you. I meant them as a peace offering.

Andrew must have spent a lot of money on these flowers. It'll mean that he'll have to go without, as he has only his student's grant to live on.

I'll be off, then. Sorry I caused such a problem with Penny.

Andrew didn't cause it. I've been unfair — very unfair! He made it worse, but he didn't cause it.

Let's forget it, Andrew. It wasn't really your fault. I'm sorry I was so nasty. Will you forgive me?

You bet!

A little later —

Those flowers look nice in that glass vase. You can see their legs through it!

I know you're just teasing — but you've given me a possible answer to Penny's problem, Andrew.

And, a few weeks later —

Go to sleep now, hyacinth bulb, 'cos sleep will help your legs grow. I can see your legs are growing nice and strong.

Now her curiosity is satisfied! Penny hasn't pulled up any flowers, since I fixed that bulb up for her.

It was because you bought me those flowers, Andrew, and made that comment, that I was able to help Penny. I can't thank you enough.

I've got all the thanks I need, just to see you happy and smiling again!

THE END

POP-A-PENNY DOODLE

IS YOUR PURSE EVER WEIGHED DOWN WITH LOOSE SMALL CHANGE? DO YOU OFTEN HAVE TOO MANY PENNY OR TWOPENNY PIECES?

EH? SHE MUST HAVE FINALLY FLIPPED!

ONLY JOKING, REALLY, BUT THAT'S HOW GROWN-UPS SOMETIMES FEEL - WEARS OUT DAD'S TROUSER POCKETS, ETC. CLICK FOR SOME EXTRA CASH BY MAKING THIS SUPER LOOSE-CHANGE CACHE THEY CAN STASH THEIR ODD COPPERS AWAY IN.

FIRST YOU NEED A BOTTLE....MILK, LEMONADE, OR WHATEVER. OURS IS AN ORANGE-JUICE BOTTLE. 20 CM. TALL BY 8 CM. DIAMETER. WRAP NON-FRAY MATERIAL ROUND, COVERING JUST ABOVE THE SHOULDER AS IN PIC (I), AND GLUE TO THE BOTTLE. TIE AND GLUE A RIBBON ROUND, AS YOU SEE IN PIC (2).

BOW-WOW!

BACK VIEW

TAIL

MEASURE MATERIAL FOR THE HEAD, 5 CM. LONGER THAN FROM THE SHOULDER TO THE BOTTLE TOP. OVERLAPPING LOOSELY ROUND AND GLUING THE OVERLAP ONLY, SO THAT YOU CAN TAKE IT ON AND OFF. TIE WOOL TO GATHER UP (3), THEN GLUE A STRIP 3X16 CM. ACROSS (4). FOR THE NOSE, ROLL A STRIP IX4 CM., GLUE, STUFF WITH COTTON-WOOL, GLUE A BLACK CARD DISC ON THE END. AND GLUE INTO PLACE (5). GLUE ON TWO CARD DISCS FOR EYES. MAKE SIX WOOLLEN BALLS AS SHOWN LEFT, WINDING 150 TIMES ROUND FINGERS (6), TYING IN A BUNDLE (7), THEN CUTTING THE LOOPS AND TRIMMING (8). GLUE ON AS TOPKNOT, FEET, AND TAIL (SEE BIG PIC). MAKE FOUR SMALLER BALLS (WINDING 100 TIMES) FOR EARS AND CHEEKS.

YOU'LL BE AMAZED HOW ATTRACTIVE IT'LL LOOK, AND HOW IT'LL ATTRACT CASH. JUST LIFT OFF HIS HEAD AND POP A PENNY IN.

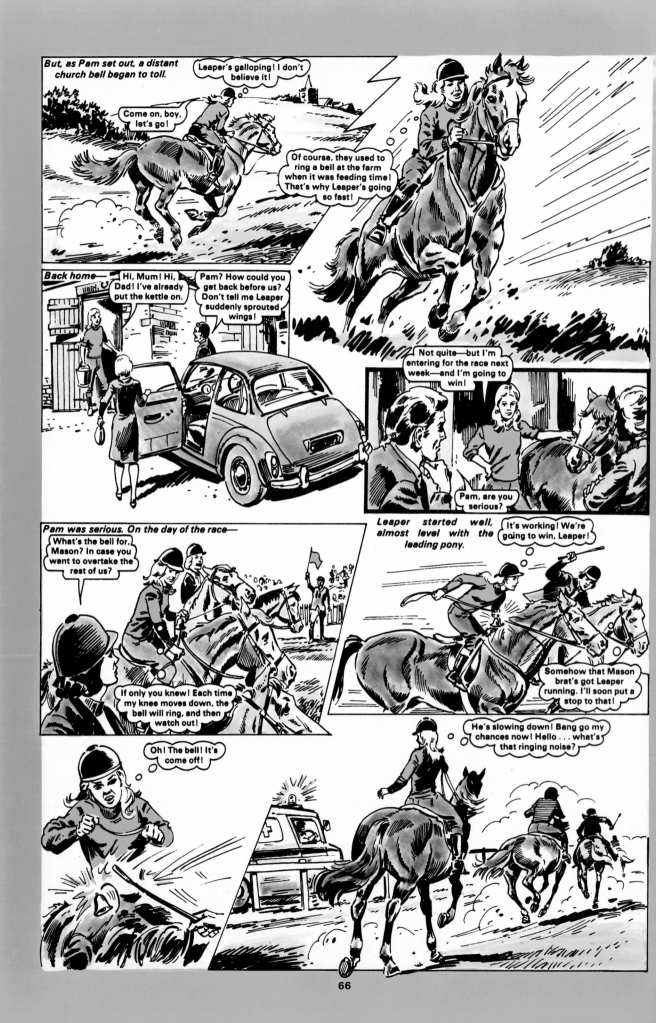

Community Nurse

CAROL HARVEY was a community nurse, based at the Daleport and District Health Centre. Carol treated patients in their own homes, and one morning she had just visited a Mrs Marley. As Carol left the house—

I see Debbie Bowen's still off school, Mr Marley.

Aye. It was only a bit of a cold the child had, but you know how her mother fusses.

There you are, Debbie! I told you to stay indoors by the fire, didn't I? Come along, dear. It's too cold to play outdoors.

It's not! I want to swing and...

OH!

Debbie!

I'm going to have two patients! Mrs Bowen sounds hysterical!

I'm coming, darling!

Mummy!

I must 'phone for an ambulance and . . .

Calm down, Mrs Bowen. Shouting won't help.

Carol took Debbie and Mrs Bowen into their house.

It's a nasty cut. I think I should take her along to the hospital.

There's no need for that, Mrs Bowen. I am a fully qualified nurse. And Debbie doesn't need an injection. Cheer up, Debbie, the cut isn't deep. You'll soon mend.

You will come to see Debbie tomorrow! Please, Nurse. Please!

All right, Mrs Bowen. I'll look in tomorrow.

Later that day, at the Health Centre, Carol discussed Mrs Bowen with the senior medical officer, Dr Hanson.

She is so over-protective, and it's bad for the child, Doctor.

Just over a year ago, Mr Bowen was killed in a 'plane crash. That's when Mrs Bowen became so over-protective.

A week or so later—

Fine! You're good as new again, and you can go back to school.

Oh, no, Nurse! I'm keeping her at home. Quite a few of the children at Debbie's school have gone down with chickenpox.

A few days later, when Carol was visiting Mrs Marley—

Something caught your eye, Nurse?

My ear, rather than my eye, Mrs Marley. Debbie is out in the garden, and she's singing. She has a very sweet voice. Pure and true.

Sweet as a lark. I hear her sometimes. Yes, Debbie loves to sing, and she's learning to play the piano, too. Her mother is teaching her. Mrs Bowen is a very good pianist.

A piano teacher, eh?

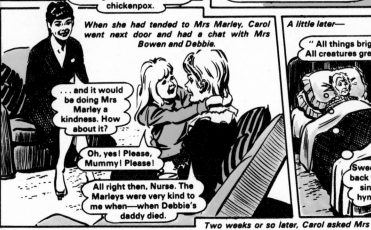

When she had tended to Mrs Marley, Carol went next door and had a chat with Mrs Bowen and Debbie.

... and it would be doing Mrs Marley a kindness. How about it?

Oh, yes! Please, Mummy! Please!

All right then, Nurse. The Marleys were very kind to me when—when Debbie's daddy died.

A little later—

"All things bright and beautiful, All creatures great and small . . ."

Sweet . . . so sweet! Takes me back to when I was a wee girl, singing this, my favourite hymn. Still is my favourite.

Thank you, my dear. You've a lovely voice and it has given an old lady a lot of pleasure.

I could come and sing to you every day if . . . Mummy? May I?

Yes, Debbie.

Two weeks or so later, Carol asked Mrs Bowen to allow Debbie to sing for the old folks at a local Home.

I'd like to—but a larger audience could be a strain on Debbie.

You could be there to accompany her at the piano, if you like. That would be a big help to her.

Please, Mrs Bowen . . . give it a try.

I can't refuse. She shall sing for the old folks.

Debbie was a great success with the old folks at the Home.

They really loved Debbie's singing—and Debbie! I do feel so proud!

Great! Now on to stage three of my plan.

Matron has been having a chat with me. She wants me to entertain the old people a couple of times a week, at the piano. I think I'll agree. It will give me an interest, and I'd like to help.

That's fine!

She'll always think the world of Debbie, but the child won't be her whole world from now on. That's a much healthier state of affairs.

THE END

71

HISTORY OF A KNOW-ALL

L ITTLE Suzy Hathersage
    Was brilliant from an early age.
In every sphere, in all endeavour,
She was particularly clever.
Before she reached the age of two
(When normal babies only " goo ")
She learned to count, and read and write . . .
Much to her parents' great delight.
She mastered calculus at three
And rediscovered geometry
At four. Her father, very glad,
Said, " Yes, she gets it from her dad!"
Her mother begged to disagree:
" Our daughter gets her brains from me!"

At twelve it had become the rule
That people came to Suzy's school,
In numbers that were epidemic,
To ask her questions academic.
Suzy, smiling sweetly bright,
Gave answers that were *always right!*

In case you thought that Suzy's skill
Was lots of fun . . . it made her ill!
Instead,those big blue eyes so clear,
Were troubled by a secret fear:
Deep down, she knew, before too long,
That she must get an answer *wrong!*

Suppose some World Association
Were given faulty information?
The consequence of such a state
Was much too bad to contemplate.

So Suzy knew she had to make
A quite deliberate mistake.
(For everybody makes one once,
From genius to dullest dunce.)
But, once she'd mouthed this fact fallacious,
She could, once more, become sagacious.

72

So, all day long she bent her mind
To matters of a phoney kind,
And, finally, young Suzy said
(And proudly, too!): " The sky is red!"

Thus, knowing her mistake was past
She, happy and relaxed, fell fast
Asleep. But, in the black of night,
A straying iron meteorite
Got all burnt up to ashy dust
And stained the stratosphere with rust.
So when poor Suzy left her bed
Next day—Alas! The sky was red!
And people said:" The truth is out—
That girl is ALWAYS RIGHT: no doubt!"

So Suzy tried to make abatement
By spouting quite the daftest statement.
She said:" Our garden birds can't fly!"
(She hadn't noticed, passing by,
A van with penguins from the zoo
Had broken down, with doors askew,
And dozens of the friendly creatures
Were eating grandmother's prize freesias).
So poor old Suzy's plan had failed;
What could she do? She never quailed.
She summoned every ounce courageous,
Saying something quite outrageous.
" I," she thought, " will tell them that
I think it's true the world is flat!"

It was across the headlines plastered,
And everyone was flabbergasted.
But Suzy was so much relieved:
That rubbish *couldn't* be believed!
She needn't worry any longer
About the threat of being wrong. A
feeling like a Royal Pardon
Sent her, free, into the garden.

But, just beyond the privet hedge,
She discovered the end of the world and

fell

off

the

73

edge.

Schoolgirl Vet

KAY BURROWS *hoped that one day she would become a vet like her brother, David. Her mother was helping with a costume for a school play when suddenly there was an agitated knocking at the door.*

This hat will be the hit of the show.

The dress is coming on nicely, too. Oh!

The callers were Mr Ainsworth, a specialist animal trainer, and his assistant, Lucy Dunlop.

I'm sorry to disturb you at this hour, Mr Burrows. I found your address in the 'phone book. I've a very sick chimp here.

AINSWORTH ANIMAL ACTORS

Bring him in.

I believe you specialise in providing trained animals for publicity schemes, films and TV commercials, Mr Ainsworth.

That's right. We've come down to stage a chimp's tea party tomorrow for the opening of the new restaurant on the sea-front. Clarence here is one of my stars.

No fever and no signs of infection— but he's obviously feeling very miserable. I think it's just a tummy upset. What have you been giving him to eat?

Oh, dear!

Did I say something wrong?

I'd better own up. It was my fault. I offered him a chocolate. He grabbed the box and ate the lot. I couldn't handle him.

Lucy! Why didn't you tell me this?

I was scared. I've only had this job a few weeks and I love it. I don't want to lose it.

Not to worry, Lucy. We'll give Clarence some medicine that will settle his stomach. I'll mix it into a bowl of porridge.

But Clarence refused to eat anything.

When Clarence is in this mood, he can be very difficult.

I'll call my sister.

Can I help?

My sister has an amazing way with animals, which often works when everything else has failed. I don't know what I'd do without her.

Kay gave Clarence her hat to wear, then—

Eat up, now. There's a good boy.

Amazing!

A good night's sleep and he'll be as right as rain.

I don't think Clarence should go back with the others while he's still feeling out of sorts.

True. We can keep him here until morning.

Kay's mother came in.

He could sleep in my room.

But what would your mother say to that?

My children have me well trained! I never know what guests to expect! Anything from snakes to tigers!

By morning, Clarence had fully recovered. David, driving to his surgery, gave Kay a lift so that she could deliver the chimp on her way to school. At the new restaurant, Kay found Mr Ainsworth's assistant in a panic.

I'm terrified! Mr Ainsworth has had to dash up to Birmingham. I've got to see this job through on my own and then drive the troupe to join him.

Relax, Lucy, I'm sure everything will be all right. It's a great chance for you to show you can be trusted.

Kay was on the point of leaving school that afternoon when she was told to report to the head teacher's room.

A message from your brother, Kay. Will you please join him at the new restaurant at once?

Can that mean Clarence has had a relapse? Poor Lucy will be worried stiff.

Kay, I'm in terrible trouble! Clarence has been difficult all day, fretting for Mr Ainsworth, but he went through the show all right, then . . .

"I'd got the others into the van and was just taking Clarence, who always likes to go last. Then someone accidentally dropped some crockery and Clarence took fright —"

David's senior partner, Duncan MacKenzie, arrived, angrily waving a newspaper.

It's hopeless! Clarence won't be caught.

Mr Ainsworth will probably fire me if I have to get him back.

David, have you seen the early edition of the evening paper?

It's all over town! We're a highly respected veterinary practice! You'll make us a laughing stock if you can't find a way to stop that animal making a fool of you!

I've had an idea. Drive me home.

You're not going to leave Clarence up there?

We'll be back as fast as we can.

When Kay returned—

Clarence! See the pretty hat!

I thought this hat would tempt him.

I'm so grateful! You've saved my job!

A few mornings later—

For you, from Mr Ainsworth, for the way you coped. And he says the restaurant manager is delighted. You made the place famous overnight. Every table is booked for weeks.

The End.

75

Make this PONY BLANKET...

DRAPE YOUR BLANKET OVER YOUR PONY, AND MARK ROUGHLY WITH CHALK WHERE TO CUT, USING THE PICTURES ABOVE AS A GUIDE. CUT AWAY AS AT FAR LEFT, THEN BIND AND STITCH THE EDGES WITH WHITE TAPE (25 MM. WIDE) AS SHOWN IN THE INSET (RIGHT).

USE THE SAME TAPE TO MAKE THE TIES, AS SHOWN ABOVE. YOU'LL NEED TO RENEW THEM FROM TIME TO TIME, BUT IT'S EASIER THAN FASTENING WEBBING OR LEATHER STRAPS.

FOR THE INITIALS OR NAME, PIN NARROW TAPE INTO POSITION, THEN SEW DOWN (INSET RIGHT). USE A SURCINGLE (WEBBING BELT) IF YOU USE THE BLANKET A GREAT DEAL AND HAVE TROUBLE KEEPING IT ON (SEE LOWER INSET).

TRANSFORM AN ORDINARY WOOL BLANKET INTO **THIS!** VERY USEFUL AND **VERY** ATTRACTIVE!

THIS IS A **DAY** BLANKET. SUPER FOR GYMKHANAS OR ANY OCCASION WHEN YOUR PONY NEEDS TO LOOK SMART.

DECORATE WITH EDGING AND YOUR INITIALS OR YOUR PONY'S NAME.

NOT TO BE CONFUSED WITH A NEW-ZEALAND RUG - WATERPROOF, LINED CANVAS TO KEEP HIM WARM AND DRY IN WINTER.

EDGING

TAPE

THE WRONG TRACK

RAILWAYMAN'S daughter Pamela Wade had won a scholarship to exclusive Wensley Grange School. Her first day there was marred by Sybilla Mentmore, the form captain.

Hello. Is this class 3b, please?

Good grief! They're letting anybody in here, these days! It's *form 3b*, peasant! We don't have a class here—and *you* certainly don't have any!

Sadly, Pamela took her place.

I suppose I should have expected this. It still hurts, though.

Peter—you *are* taking me to the school disco on Saturday, aren't you?

At break—

Hi! You must be Pam Wade. I'm Peter Graham. Welcome to Wensley. It's a bit crumbling, but it's all right.

Thanks, Peter. It looks fine to me.

He's a lot nicer than his girlfriend!

Later—

Bother! The heel's come away!

What's the matter, Wade? Daddy can't afford decent shoes?

For goodness sake, Sybilla, stop picking on Pam! It's tough enough getting used to a new school without your smart remarks!

Peter!

He's all right, that Peter Graham. I wish it were me he was taking to the disco tomorrow.

But Pamela went alone.

Hey, look everybody! The peasant's been at Mummy's rag-bag! Or have you robbed a scarecrow, Wade?

How could she be so cruel?

Pamela ran outside in tears.

It's no use! I'll have to ask Mum and Dad if I can go back to my old school!

Pam! Don't go. Sybilla's just a born loudmouth.

Look, we're having a garden party at our place on Sunday afternoon. Why not come along? Sybilla's not going to be there.

Oh, I'd love to, Peter, thank you!

On Sunday, Pamela felt a bit ill-at-ease, but—

Pam! Come on, I'll show you around—but let me get you a cola first.

Great! Lovely garden you have here!

Maybe—but not when you have to mow the lawns! Come on—I've some records in the summer house.

Thanks.

All too soon, it was time to leave.

We're going to the town bicentenary celebrations next Saturday. Like to come with us?

Love to! I'll meet you outside the school at two.

Back home—

I'm back, Mum.

Oh, Pam, your father's working a late shift at the railway yard. Will you take his lunch down to him?

Pamela found her father working on an old steam engine.

Hello, Pam. What d'you think of this, eh? They've asked me to drive it for the town's celebrations.

That's fantastic, Dad! You'll be the star of the show!

But, as Pamela left—

You think you're great because you were invited to Peter's party and I wasn't! How d'you think he's going to act when he learns that your father's a common railwayman?

I'm proud of my dad! And if Peter doesn't like it, that's just too bad! I'll tell him at school tomorrow!

But Peter wasn't at school the following day.

No, Peter Graham won't be here this week. We had a note from his father.

Lucky for the peasant! But it won't do her any good! I'm going round there tonight!

But Pamela saw Peter in the town that evening.

Peter!

He's avoiding me! Sybilla must have got to him already! I didn't think he'd be so like her!

Nevertheless, Pamela waited outside the school, as they had arranged, the next Saturday.

Perhaps he'll still come.

Peter!

Hi, Pamela! Hop in!

78

They drove to the railway embankment.

Sorry about running away from you the other day. I wasn't supposed to be out. My cousin had mumps and I was in quarantine.

So Sybilla hasn't seen Peter! No-one has!

Before Pamela could reply, there was an announcement

Ladies and gentlemen, a classic from the age of steam!

Hi there, Pamela!

Hi, Dad!

Pamela! Is that your father . . . driving the train?

Pamela was proud of her dad.

Yes, that's my dad. He's a railwayman.

It's the Craigenna Castle, 4-6-0, Castle Class, Great Western Railway!

Would he . . . would he let us have a closer look?

Come on up. You can drive her, if you like.

Surprised, Pamela introduced the Grahams to her father.

Drive her? You don't mean it? It's always been my dream!

Hurry up, Dad!

A few minutes later—

Pam! You never told me your father was a railwayman!

Well, you never asked me. Look . . . there's Sybilla. Hi, Sybilla.

Well!

The next weekend, the Wades were guests at the Graham house.

You've got the Royal Scot nameplate? I drove her on the anniversary run to Glasgow.

I was on that run! We're practically old friends, George!

Men and trains! Where will it end?

They never grow up, Elizabeth!

Have a cake, Pam. I think my dad's got yours here for the night!

Sybilla thought that Peter was as narrow-minded and snobbish as herself—but she really was on the wrong track!

THE END

79

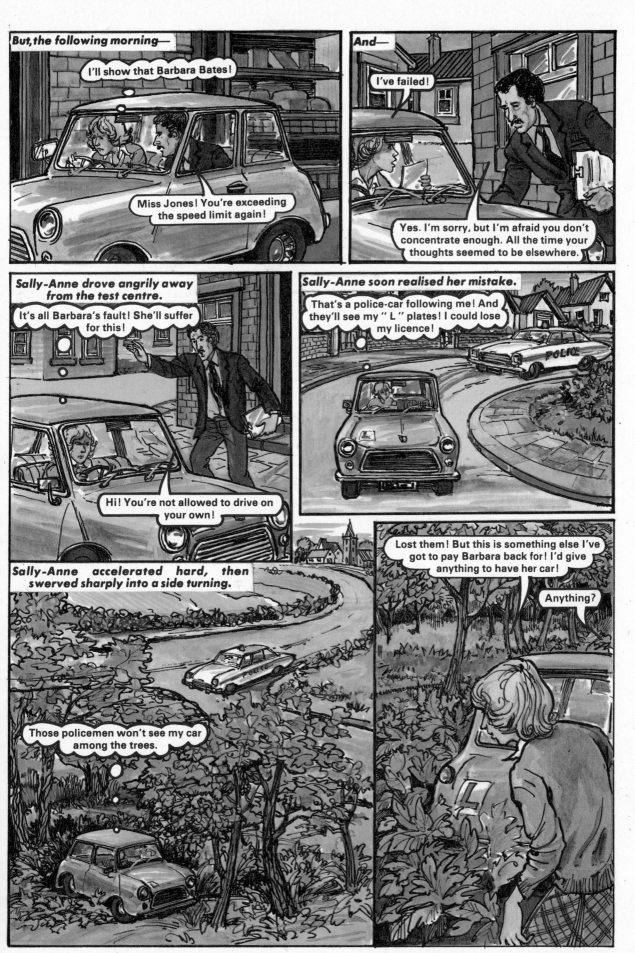

And there's Barbara with my old car! She'll have failed her test! I can hardly wait!

Hi, everybody! Fancy a drive? I passed my driving test!

Oh, hello, Sally-Anne. Barbara failed her test.

I'm not surprised in that old heap of a thing! Besides, you've got to have a natural talent for driving, like I have!

Then Sally-Anne caught sight of her reflection in the car window and realised it was not only the cars that had changed owners.

Do you think so, Sally-Anne?

Wh . . . what's happened? You . . . you have my face!

No! I only wanted the car! Not her awful pudgy face! Barbara—you must know what's happened to us!

What's Sally-Anne going on about? Do you know, Barbara?

Haven't the faintest idea. But, you know, I never did like Sally-Anne very much in the first place.

THE END.

85

JUDY 1985

JANUARY

S		6	13	20	27
M		7	14	21	28
Tu	1	8	15	22	29
W	2	9	16	23	30
Th	3	10	17	24	31
F	4	11	18	25	
S	5	12	19	26	

FEBRUARY

S		3	10	17	24
M		4	11	18	25
Tu		5	12	19	26
W		6	13	20	27
Th		7	14	21	28
F	1	8	15	22	
S	2	9	16	23	

MARCH

S		3	10	17	24	31
M		4	11	18	25	
Tu		5	12	19	26	
W		6	13	20	27	
Th		7	14	21	28	
F	1	8	15	22	29	
S	2	9	16	23	30	

JUDY 1985

APRIL

S		7	14	21	28
M	1	8	15	22	29
Tu	2	9	16	23	30
W	3	10	17	24	
Th	4	11	18	25	
F	5	12	19	26	
S	6	13	20	27	

MAY

S		5	12	19	26
M		6	13	20	27
Tu		7	14	21	28
W	1	8	15	22	29
Th	2	9	16	23	30
F	3	10	17	24	31
S	4	11	18	25	

JUNE

S		2	9	16	23	30
M		3	10	17	24	
Tu		4	11	18	25	
W		5	12	19	26	
Th		6	13	20	27	
F		7	14	21	28	
S	1	8	15	22	29	

JUDY 1985

JULY				
S		7	14	21	28
M	1	8	15	22	29
Tu	2	9	16	23	30
W	3	10	17	24	31
Th	4	11	18	25	
F	5	12	19	26	
S	6	13	20	27	

AUGUST				
S		4	11	18	25
M		5	12	19	26
Tu		6	13	20	27
W		7	14	21	28
Th	1	8	15	22	29
F	2	9	16	23	30
S	3	10	17	24	31

SEPTEMBER				
S	1	8	15	22	29
M	2	9	16	23	30
Tu	3	10	17	24	
W	4	11	18	25	
Th	5	12	19	26	
F	6	13	20	27	
S	7	14	21	28	

JUDY 1985

OCTOBER

S		6	13	20	27
M		7	14	21	28
Tu	1	8	15	22	29
W	2	9	16	23	30
Th	3	10	17	24	31
F	4	11	18	25	
S	5	12	19	26	

NOVEMBER

S		3	10	17	24
M		4	11	18	25
Tu		5	12	19	26
W		6	13	20	27
Th		7	14	21	28
F	1	8	15	22	29
S	2	9	16	23	30

DECEMBER

S	1	8	15	22	29
M	2	9	16	23	30
Tu	3	10	17	24	31
W	4	11	18	25	
Th	5	12	19	26	
F	6	13	20	27	
S	7	14	21	28	

Half a mile away—

A gorilla tribe has passed this way recently, Dr Forrester.

Excellent, Salifu! We'll try to pick them up in the morning. Time for bed, Linda.

All right, Dad.

Later—

I just can't get to sleep. I'll have a look in the forest. Perhaps I'll see a gorilla in the distance. No-one will notice if I'm not long.

Linda foolishly wandered deep into the jungle.

It is a human—I just know it! What a strange creature—draped with coloured, woven grasses!

Linda was lost—and that wasn't all.

I can't find the path back! All the trees look the same!

The panther is about to spring—and the human has not noticed! I must do something!

The panther and Oona moved at the same moment.

Aaaaaah!

Go! This human is not food for you tonight!

92

A gorilla! It saved me—and now it's pointing the way! It looks almost intelligent!

The human's eyes are like ours—looks almost intelligent!

Oona led Linda to safety.

The forest is no place for you, human. Stay with your people.

Linda? Is that you? Where have you been?

Both young females were in trouble.

Stay by your mother's side, in future!

Don't you leave the camp again!

Two days later, the hunters caught up with the tribe.

Humans! Run for the trees! Take cover, children!

I've hit the young female with the dart! Get her in the net!

Oona felt the tranquillising dart enter her leg.

My leg . . . I have been bitten . . . I . . . I . . . cannot . . . stand up . . .

Good work! Keep firing in the air to frighten the others away A perfect specimen for the zoo.

Dr Forrester returned to camp, well pleased with his prize.

A superb catch . . . a young female. Go and have a look, Linda . . . she's still asleep.

It's the gorilla that helped me!

Dad, why are the men loading their rifles?

The mother always comes to try to get her child back. I'm afraid we may have to shoot the mother.

That night—

Dad will be furious—but I'm not letting them take that animal to the zoo, or letting them shoot her mother!

Linda silently opened the cage.

It is the human I saw in the woods. Has she come to release me? Mother is nearby. I heard her call.

Linda led Oona to the edge of the forest, then—

Go on—you're free!

She seems to want me to go with her.

Linda followed Oona and—

Oona! You are free!

Yes, mother, the human freed me. It is a young one, like me.

But Salifu's eyes were better accustomed to the jungle night than Forrester's.

No, Dr Forrester—that is not a fighting posture! Do not fire! You could hit your daughter!

But Linda's absence had been noticed.

There they are!

That adult's going to crush Linda!

94

BRENDA JONES was one of the biggest girls at Woodley Grammar School— and the least popular.

Hey! that's my chocolate, Brenda!

It's mine now, Shirley. Want to complain?

Softy Simpson

Just then, the bell rang for morning lessons.

That Brenda Jones gets away with murder. It's time somebody taught her a lesson.

But who? She's the strongest girl in the class!

Soon—

Good morning, girls, this is Stella Simpson, your new classmate. She can have the desk next to Brenda.

She looks a right muggins.

The teacher began a French lesson by asking the girls to name various objects in French.

Qu'est-ce que c'est, Brenda?

Oh—er—half past nine, miss.

Really, Brenda, you haven't been paying attention! Can anyone give the correct answer?

C'est une plume, madame.

Well done, Stella—a pen. I only wish you could impart some of your knowledge to Brenda.

Serves Brenda right—but Stella's made a dangerous enemy there.

At break time—

So—teacher's pet already, Simpson! Well, since you're so clever at French, you can do the translation I was given as a punishment—or I'll make you sorry!

I didn't mean to get you into trouble, but I'll do that exercise for you.

After that, Brenda seldom left Stella in peace.

Oh!

So sorry! Accidents will happen!

And later—

Who wrote this?

I did, as a matter of fact. It's the truth, isn't it?

SoFTY SIMPSON HA HA HA!

Stella's letting Brenda away with it again.

Yeah, but at least, with Brenda picking on Stella all the time, things have been easier for us lately!

Then, one morning, as Stella approached the school—

That looks suspicious. Brenda seems to be taking money from that kid.

But, when Stella challenged Brenda—

Not that it's any of your business, but I look after my cousin June's pocket-money to make sure it lasts her all week.

Oh—er, sorry.

A few days later—

It's June, isn't it— Brenda's cousin? What's the matter?

100

THE END

WHEEL OF FORTUNE

HAVE YOU A PROBLEM? DO YOU NEED ADVICE? DO YOU WONDER WHAT THE FUTURE HOLDS? JUST CLOSE YOUR EYES, TURN ROUND THREE TIMES (ANTI-CLOCKWISE), AND CHOOSE ANY NUMBER FROM ONE TO EIGHT.

THEN WORK ROUND THE SPIRAL FROM "**START**", WRITING DOWN THE LETTERS APPEARING WITH YOUR NUMBER.

TRACE OFF AND PASTE THIS DISC ONTO CARD, AND CARRY IT WITH YOU ALWAYS!

ROLL UP! ROLL UP! SEE WHAT'S IN STORE FOR YOU AND YOUR FRIENDS!

EACH PERSON MAY ASK ONLY ONE QUESTION PER DAY.

BOBBY DAZZLER

BOBBY DAZZLER was the only girl at Westbury Boarding School for Boys, where her mother was matron. Bobby claimed that anything the boys could do, she could do better.

Westbury has been invited to enter a big athletics meeting at the town sports ground on the eighteenth. We must hold some trials to choose our team.

Great! I can hardly wait!

Huh! Some hopes Bobby has!

Half an hour later—

Dead heat for Bobby and Mike. I wonder which of them I should select.

You've already won a place in the one hundred-metres sprint, Mike, so I think it would be fairer to let Bobby represent us in the hurdling event.

Huh! Hurdling's my favourite!

It's not fair, Don! Downright favouritism!

I've just remembered something! Mike's in luck this time!

Sorry, Steve—I'm afraid I shan't be able to run for Westbury after all. I've promised to sing a solo in the annual choral competition that day—and I can't let them down now.

That's great news!

On the day before the athletics meeting—

Guess what? Our races are going to be on TV!

Fantastic! With a bit of luck, we'll see ourselves on one of the evening programmes!

Next day—

Good luck, everyone! Bring back lots of trophies!

It's a shame you're not coming, Bobby—but you can watch us tonight on telly!

Trust Mike! He's more interested in being on television than winning his race, if you ask me!

Ten minutes later—

Oh, no! Mike's forgotten his running shoes! Of all the silly chumps!

The sports ground isn't far from my concert hall. With luck, I'll get Mike's shoes to him in time.

But when she arrived—

If I've got to squeeze through all these crowds, I'll never reach Mike in time! There's only one thing for it . . .

Meanwhile—

This is terrible! No-one else's shoes fit me! I can't run without shoes!

LOOK, MIKE!

It's—it's Bobby!

With *your* shoes, Mike!

May I have a word with you, miss?

Yes, but I don't have much time.

That evening—

Come and sit by me, Bobby. The sports programme begins soon.

Not a sign of us, Don! Of all the luck!

But as the programme ended—

And lastly . . . Bobby Dazzler in her valiant effort to save her team-mate's chances in the match!

I don't believe it!

So Bobby's stolen the limelight again!

That girl should be locked up!

THE END

103

ANIMAL QUIZ

QUESTIONS:

1. Nicknamed Brock.
2. If you chatter a lot, you are supposed to be talking the hind legs off a . . .
3. Type of pony favoured by cowboys and Indians.
4. If you arrive late, in some places people say: "You're all behind, like the cow's . . ."
5. You might be giddy as a . . . .
6. Or, mad as a March . . . .
7. Large breed of dog associated with aid in the Alps.
8. Wild horses of Australia.
9. Supposed to be lucky, when it's absolutely black. What is it?
10. It comes from the Arctic region and is beloved of circuses and zoos.
11. Mythical winged horse.
12. The breed name for an Alsatian dog.

ANSWERS: 1. Badger. 2. Donkey. 3. Mustang. 4. Tail. 5. Goat. 6. Hare. 7. St. Bernard. 8. Brumbies. 9. A cat. 10. Polar Bear. 11. Pegasus. 12. German Shepherd dog.

The GIRL with the GOLDEN SMILE

I've been saving up to buy that lovely china cat, Sandra. When I get my pay packet today, I should have enough. Like it?

Very much. Come on, Anna, or we'll be late checking in.

ANNA MARSHALL, a junior trainee at Westerby's department store, found her work interesting, as she changed departments frequently. One morning, on her way to work, Anna stopped her friend, Sandra, at one of the windows of Westerby's.

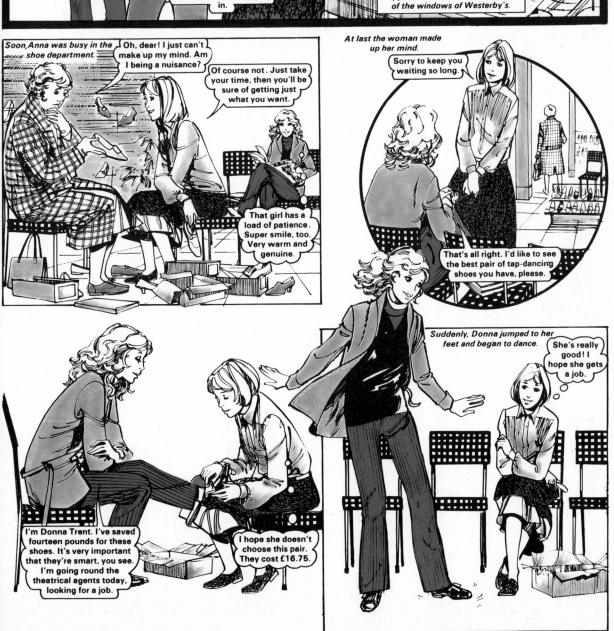

Soon, Anna was busy in the shoe department.

Oh, dear! I just can't make up my mind. Am I being a nuisance?

Of course not. Just take your time, then you'll be sure of getting just what you want.

That girl has a load of patience. Super smile, too. Very warm and genuine.

At last the woman made up her mind.

Sorry to keep you waiting so long.

That's all right. I'd like to see the best pair of tap-dancing shoes you have, please.

Suddenly, Donna jumped to her feet and began to dance.

She's really good! I hope she gets a job.

I'm Donna Trent. I've saved fourteen pounds for these shoes. It's very important that they're smart, you see. I'm going round the theatrical agents today, looking for a job.

I hope she doesn't choose this pair. They cost £16.75.

As Anna had hoped, Donna's performance was noticed by Harry Wilkie.

Ladies and gentlemen, I must apologise for the delay, due to a technical hitch. But, in the meantime, we're providing some entertainment.

That girl is quite remarkable, isn't she, dear?

Yes, indeed.

After the dance was finished, Mr Wilkie had a word with Donna.

I liked your act, Donna, and I wonder if you'd be interested in dancing at the Coliseum in my new show, starting Monday.

Oh, thank you, Mr Wilkie! I'd love to!

Time for me to get back to the shoe department—before I get asked a lot of awkward questions!

Next morning, in the office of Miss Morris, who was in charge of the trainees at Westerby's—

Well, Anna, you've certainly proved yourself a most enterprising young woman. You did very well to provide a fill-in for the fashion show at such short notice—but, tell me, if you were in the shoe department, how did you know all was not well at the show?

Er . . .

It's all right, Anna. Donna told me all about it. You're forgiven—under the circumstances. Now, here's Donna to see you.

Hi, Anna! This is for you—for helping me to get my contract.

The china cat! How on earth did you guess it was just what I was wanting?

Oh, I thought it was the kind of thing you'd like.

It's lucky I was standing outside the store yesterday when she was telling her friend about the cat!

I said the new shoes might bring me luck, Anna, and they did—but only because through buying them, I met you! Thanks!

THE END

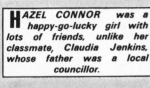

REAL MONEY

HAZEL CONNOR was a happy-go-lucky girl with lots of friends, unlike her classmate, Claudia Jenkins, whose father was a local councillor.

Sorry I'm late, Miss. It was—um—

Oh, don't apologise, Hazel! It's good of you to drop in at school from time to time! Now, do you mind if we get on with the lesson?

We're having a special fund-raising drive on behalf of the local children's charity. The pupil who raises the most money will win a splendid trophy donated by Claudia's father.

Ask your relatives and friends if you can do odd jobs for them for a small sum, and fill in their names in these cards.

Sounds fun!

Fun, she says! Charity work isn't supposed to be *fun!*

Claudia's father was president of a local charity.

At break—

I expect to win the trophy, of course. My father's going to pay me ten pounds to clean his car.

That's not fair!

Surely, winning the trophy isn't as important as helping the charity?

Just the sort of thing I expect from your kind, Hazel Connor! That's why you'll never have any real money!

Typical, isn't it? Her rich dad donates a trophy—then makes sure that *she'll* be the one to win it!

Never mind. It *will* be a lot of fun, and we'll all be able to raise a bit of money, won't we?

Hazel set to work that evening.

You're doing a grand job, Hazel. I can't cope with weeding since my back trouble.

Oh, I like gardening— especially for you, Uncle Bert!

Only twenty pence? Is that enough? You've done a lot of work.

I enjoyed it. Will you sign the card for me?

Shining at last!

And Hazel's classmates worked hard, too.

Nearly finished!

All except Claudia.

Come along, put your backs into it! I'm not paying you twenty-five pence each to take it easy!

Later—

It looks like new, Claudia! You must have worked hard!

Well, it's all for the good of the charity, isn't it, Father?

The day before the money was to be handed in, the girls compared notes.

I managed to get three pounds forty. How about you?

Three pounds sixty-eight. None of us is going to be anywhere near what Claudia's got.

Never mind, we did the best we could, and the kids will get the benefit.

Yes, but it still doesn't seem right.

After school, as Hazel walked home—

They're right, it's not fair, but . . . Oh! That dog's going to be run over!

Hazel snatched the dog to safety.

Got you! That driver must be asleep! Gosh, my money's flying away!

I'll never get it back now, and all because of you, doggie! I suppose I'd better find out where you're from and take you home.

MAKE IT FROM REALLY STOUT CARD, PASTING THE "BUG" ON AND CUTTING OUT (OR TRACE OFF). SCORE ALONG THE DOTTED LINES, THEN MAKE ANOTHER EXACTLY THE SAME. LAY THEM FLAT TOGETHER, BUT SO THAT THE POINTS OF ONE COINCIDE WITH THE SPACES OF THE OTHER (TOP LEFT). WEAVE A SMALL RUBBER BAND TIGHTLY ROUND THE POINTS AS SHOWN, THEN WATCH IT BECOME A SOLID BALL!

EMERGENCY SLIPPERS

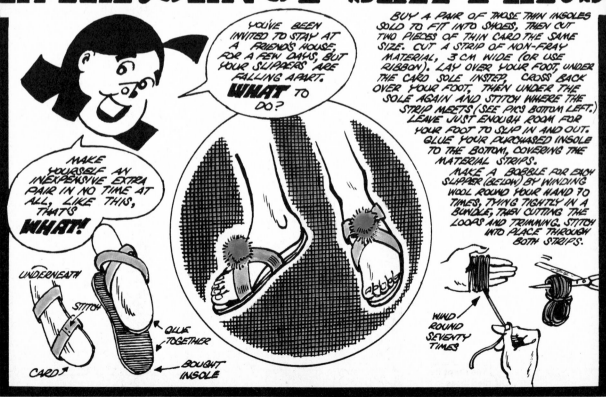

BUY A PAIR OF THOSE THIN INSOLES SOLD TO FIT INTO SHOES, THEN CUT TWO PIECES OF THIN CARD THE SAME SIZE. CUT A STRIP OF NON-FRAY MATERIAL, 3 CM WIDE (OR USE RIBBON). LAY OVER YOUR FOOT, UNDER THE CARD SOLE INSTEP, CROSS BACK OVER YOUR FOOT, THEN UNDER THE SOLE AGAIN AND STITCH WHERE THE STRIP MEETS (SEE PICS BOTTOM LEFT.) LEAVE JUST ENOUGH ROOM FOR YOUR FOOT TO SLIP IN AND OUT. GLUE YOUR PURCHASED INSOLE TO THE BOTTOM, COVERING THE MATERIAL STRIPS.

MAKE A BOBBLE FOR EACH SLIPPER (BELOW) BY WINDING WOOL ROUND YOUR HAND 70 TIMES, TYING TIGHTLY IN A BUNDLE, THEN CUTTING THE LOOPS AND TRIMMING. STITCH INTO PLACE THROUGH BOTH STRIPS.

114

Millions of people in Britain have spent a holiday at a Butlin's Holiday Camp, so we decided to send Clare and our photographer to the camp at Bognor Regis to find out just what took place on a typical holiday week there and why so many people were content to . . .

CARRY ON CAMPING!

Much of the camp life revolves around the swimming pools—you can make a splash in either the outdoor or indoor pool — and once you've paid for your holiday, most things are free.

There's an amusement arcade where you can spend all day whizzing down slides, if that's what you fancy.

There's free sports coaching, too. Clare couldn't wait to use the trampoline .

Clare also took the opportunity to try fencing. It calls for quick thinking and is exciting.

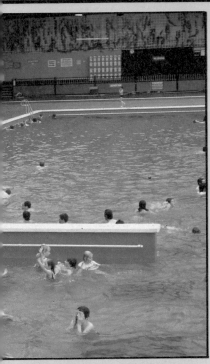

Even if you don't want to enter the disco-dancing competition, you'll probably want to join in the dancing. Clare certainly did.

And no holiday is complete without at least one ride on the dodgems. It's all part of the holiday spirit.

Of course, making friends is all part of the holiday fun. Clare and her new-found friend, Mandy, enjoyed a ride at the fairground.

The shows given by Butlin's Redcoats are justly famous. Some well-known stars have worked at Butlin's. The Butlin's Gaiety Theatre at Bognor Regis has 1800 seats and a stage a foot wider than the one in the London Palladium. The Children's Theatre seats 600. That's a lot of people to entertain!

One thing is sure—at a holiday camp, you won't find the evenings boring. There's so much to do, it's making the choice that's difficult. And if you don't enjoy dressing up, it can be just as much fun to watch the fancy-dress competition.

All good things come to an end, however, and, all too soon, it was time for Clare to leave. But six out of ten people at Butlin's on any holiday week have been there before—and Clare was determined that she, too, would return.

Please buy me...

Won't somebody, please, come and buy me?
I'm such a cute puppy, you see,
With my velvet-brown eyes
and my sad little sighs,
I'm as lonesome as lonesome can be.

I've got floppy ears and a short, stumpy tail,
And I'm friendly to all who are kind;
You'll see, in the house, I'm as quiet as a mouse,
So what better pup could you find?

Won't somebody please come and buy me?
I'm a well-behaved chap, you'll agree.
I won't chase the cat, or leave bones on the mat—
A model of models, that's me!

Won't somebody please make me happy?
There's only one thing that I need.
So, please, if as yet, you haven't a pet,
Take me home with a collar and lead

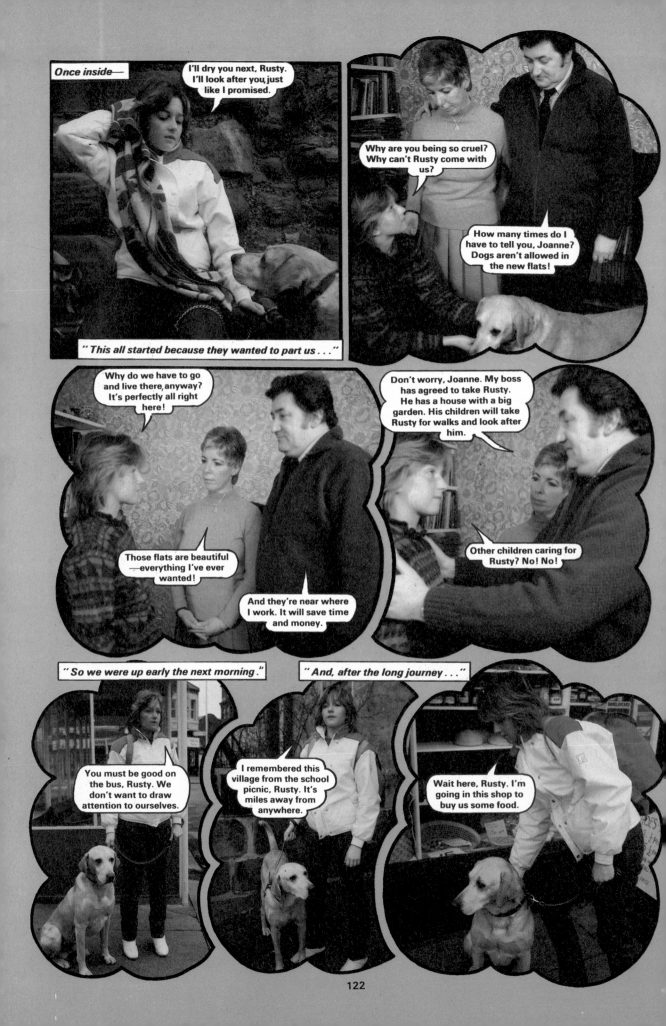

Once inside—

I'll dry you next, Rusty. I'll look after you, just like I promised.

"This all started because they wanted to part us..."

Why are you being so cruel? Why can't Rusty come with us?

How many times do I have to tell you, Joanne? Dogs aren't allowed in the new flats!

Why do we have to go and live there, anyway? It's perfectly all right here!

Those flats are beautiful —everything I've ever wanted!

And they're near where I work. It will save time and money.

Don't worry, Joanne. My boss has agreed to take Rusty. He has a house with a big garden. His children will take Rusty for walks and look after him.

Other children caring for Rusty? No! No!

"So we were up early the next morning."

"And, after the long journey..."

You must be good on the bus, Rusty. We don't want to draw attention to ourselves.

I remembered this village from the school picnic, Rusty. It's miles away from anywhere.

Wait here, Rusty. I'm going in this shop to buy us some food.

Later—

The rain's stopped, so why don't we pretend that we really are on holiday, Rusty? Let's go and explore.

So—

Look, Rusty . . . the beach!

This is great!

But, suddenly—

Oh, Rusty . . . I feel so hot! Must be all this running about .

No—it's not just that. I don't feel very well. We'd better get back to the castle . . .

I've probably caught a slight chill. But don't worry Rusty . . . I'll feel better tomorrow . . . we'll move on somewhere new . . . I'll get a job of some kind . . . I won't let them part us . . .

Once back in the ruin, Joanne felt worse and worse.

Then Joanne remembered no more.

125

"FEET" OF HIMALAYAN BALSAM

FUCHSIA

RED ADMIRAL BUTTERFLY

ORMER OR EAR SHELLS